Contents

Part One   Think Big

◇ Award-winning
  book or author

Part Two　Something Little

Part Three   On the Land

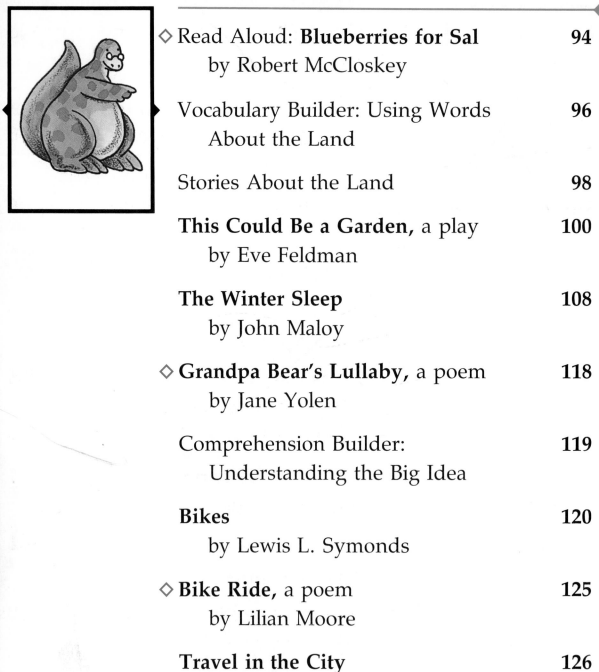

◇ Award-winning
   book or author

Part Four   On the Sea

When You Read

I like to read.
Reading is fun.
I know things that can help you read.

Before You Read

Look at the pictures.
Think about what you will read.

8

As You Read

◆ Stop when you need to.

◆ Think about what you are reading.

◆ Think about what could come after.

At times, you see a word you do
not know.
Try this:

1. Try to say the word.

2. Read the words before and after
the word.

3. Look up the word in the Pictionary
at the back of the book.

4. Get help.

After You Read

◆ Tell about the story.

The Big Brag

PART ONE

Think Big

I can do it better than you can.

Name the big things you see in
the picture.
What other big things can you
tell about?

Make a Story

Use the names of big things to finish the story.

Pat wanted to ride on the _____.
She went to a big _____.
There she saw a _____.

As You Read

In this part of the book you will read about people and animals who are big.
You will read about people and animals who make big plans, too.

Keep a Reader's Log.
Make notes in the log about what you read.
You can put in the names of big things that you know about.
If you find a new word in a story, you can put it in the log.

Big Things

Do you like big things?
I do.
I like elephants because they
are big.
I like big things because I am big.
What big things do you like?

I like to plan big things, too.
I think about what I want to make.
Then I make a plan.
With a plan, I can make something big.
Make a plan.
Think big and see what you can make.

The Little Parade

by Teresa Marquez

Fran said, "This is a good day for a
parade.
The more people we have, the more
fun it will be.
Who wants to be in a parade?"

"I do," said Pat.

"I do not want to be in the parade,"
said Tim.
"This parade is too little."

"We will have more fun if you
are in the parade," said Fran.
"But if you do not want to go with us,
go to the bridge at the end of town.
You can wait for us there."

"I will go to the bridge and
wait for you there," said Tim.

Pat got a drum from home.
Fran got a flag and waved it.
It was time for the little parade to
get going.

"This parade looks like fun!" said a
man on a horse.
"Can I be in the parade, too?"

"Yes, you can," said Pat.
"You can ride the horse in the parade.'

The man on the horse followed Pat.
Pat played the drum.
Fran waved the flag.
The little parade went on.

"This parade looks like fun!" said a
woman with a flute.
"Can I be in the parade, too?"

"Yes, you can," said Fran.
"You can play the flute."

The woman played the flute.
The man on the horse followed Pat.
Pat played the drum.
Fran waved the flag.
The little parade went on.

"Look at that parade!" said the
people in the town.
"Can we be in the parade, too?"

"Yes, you can," said Pat.
"You can all sing a song."

The people sang.
The woman played the flute.
The man on the horse followed Pat.
Pat played the drum.
Fran waved the flag.

20

The parade went to the bridge at the end of town.
Tim was waiting there.

"The parade got big," said Tim.
"Can I be in the parade?"

◆ **Think** How did the little parade get to be a big parade?

◆ **Share** Do you think Tim had more fun than Fran?

◆ **Write** Write about what you like best in a parade.

Oona and the Bad Giant

by Jacqueline Maloy

Bad Giant was a giant who was very big and very strong and very bad.

Finn MacCool was a giant, too. Finn was not as big and not as strong as Bad Giant. Finn was not bad at all.

Bad Giant wanted to show Finn just how strong he was.

Finn MacCool had a wife named Oona.
She could hear very well.

"Bad Giant wants to see
you," said Oona to Finn.
"I can hear him."

"What can I do?" said Finn.
"I do not have time to run away."

"Do not run away," said Oona.
"I can take care of him."
Oona made a rock look like a cake.

23

Then she put a baby's hat on Finn.
She made him sit in a baby's bed.

"Stay there," she said.
"Bad Giant will think you are a baby.
I will take care of Bad Giant.
Can you tell me why Bad Giant is
so big and strong?"

"Bad Giant is big and strong because
he has a big ring," said Finn.

Bad Giant came to the house.

"I am looking for Finn MacCool,"
said Bad Giant.

"Finn is not home," said Oona.
"I am Finn's wife.
This is Finn's baby.
We are waiting for Finn to get back.
He is away, looking for a giant named
Bad Giant."

"I am Bad Giant," said Bad Giant.
"I will wait for him."

Bad Giant looked at Finn in the
baby's bed.
"That is a very big baby," he said.

"Yes, but he is not as big as
Finn MacCool," said Oona.

"He is not as big and strong as I am,"
said Bad Giant.

"You do look strong," said Oona.
"Can you take me and the baby to the
lake for a drink?"

"Get on my back," said Bad Giant.
"I will take you and the baby to
the lake."

"Finn can do better than that.
He brings the house with us.
The baby and I ride in the house.
Can you do that?" said Oona.

"If Finn can do it, so can I," Bad
Giant said.
Bad Giant took the house to the lake.
Then he put it down very fast.

"There," he said, "I can do what
Finn MacCool can do."

"That was very good," said Oona.
"Take this good cake that I made.
Finn and the baby like this cake."

It was the rock that looked like a cake.
Bad Giant could not eat it.
"Who can eat a cake like this?"
he said.

"Why, Finn and the baby can eat cakes like this," said Oona.
"See, the baby wants more."

Finn, in the baby's hat, was eating a cake that was not made of rocks.

"How can a baby eat this cake?"
said Bad Giant.

Then he went to look at Finn.

"Grab the ring!" said Oona.

"I have it!" said Finn MacCool.

"Now I will not be as big and
strong as I was," said Bad Giant.

30

"You took good care of me, Oona," said Finn.

"I took care of Bad Giant, too," said Oona.

- **Think** How did Oona take good care of Finn?

- **Share** Find a part of the story that you think is funny. Read it to the class.

- **Write** Write a sentence. Tell what you liked best about Oona's big plan to help Finn.

Sizes

If you were as big as a giant flea,
How much would you have to
grow to be
The size of the tiniest head-to-tail
Very most midgety baby whale?

I mean to say—and it's no surprise—
Whatever you do about your size,
There's always something a size or two
Very much bigger or smaller than you.

I mean to say, what's big of some
Is small of others. Now get along
home.
And whether you stay or wander far,
Be just the size of whatever you are.

John Ciardi

Understanding
What Happens and Why

for **Mr. Ant and the Mailbox** and **The Brave Tailor**

What is happening in the pictures?

Thinking About What Happens and Why

The boy went for a swim because he was hot.

One thing made the other thing happen.

As You Read

Ask yourself: What happened and why did it happen in the next two stories.

Look at the words in blue to help you.

Mr. Ant and the Mailbox

by Audrey S. Driggs

This story is about an ant.

One day, Mr. George I. Ant moved to
a big house in a little town.
No one saw him when he moved in
because they were still in bed.

Think about what Mr. Ant puts on the mailbox.

"I will paint my name on my mailbox,"
said Mr. Ant.
"But I cannot put all of my name.
I will paint a G and an I and ANT."

When he had painted the mailbox,
Mr. Ant took a nap.
When he got up, Mr. Ant went to look
for friends.

He looked and looked, but he saw no
one in the little town.
Mr. Ant was scared.
Why was there no one there?

Think about why
there is no one
in the town.

Then Mr. Ant saw a big red ant.
The ant had a big club.
Now Mr. Ant was very scared.

"I am looking for the giant who
just moved to town," said Red Ant.
"All of my friends are scared, so they
want me to find him.
He has moved to the biggest house."

"That can't be!" said Mr. Ant.
"I just moved to the biggest house!"

Red Ant and Mr. Ant went to Mr. Ant's house.

"See," said Mr. Ant, "there is not a giant in that house."

"Yes, there is," said Red Ant. "Don't you see GIANT painted on the mailbox?"

Red Ant thinks there is a giant because of what he saw on the mailbox.

"Now I see why you think there is a giant in my house," said Mr. Ant. "Wait, I will get paint and you will see. All I need to do is make two dots."

Mr. George I. Ant painted two dots on the mailbox.
With the dots, Mr. Ant's name looked like this:

G.I.ANT

"I see why you were looking for a giant," said Mr. Ant.
"You did not know that I was George I. Ant because you saw GIANT on my mailbox!"

"You are so little," said Red Ant.
"Why did you move to the biggest house in town?"

Think about what Mr. Ant will tell Red Ant.

"I need a big house because I have a
wife and many little ants," said Mr. Ant.

"I am glad you are not a giant,"
said Red Ant.
"Now we can be friends."

◆ **Think**   Why did Red Ant get scared
when he saw Mr. Ant's mailbox?

◆ **Share**   What if Mr. Ant had painted
the name on the mailbox with more
care?

◆ **Write**   Write a sentence. Tell how
you can show people that you
want to be friends.

The Brave Tailor

by Dinah Anastasio

There was a tailor in Little Town.
One day, this tailor wanted cake.
There were many flies on the cake.

"Get away from my cake, flies,"
he said.
The tailor hit the flies.

"I got seven flies," he said.
"I want all the people in Big Town to
know about this!"

The tailor made a big belt that
said, "Seven at One Time."
He went to Big Town.
The people in Big Town saw the belt.

"He got seven at one time, but seven
what?" said a woman.
The people did not think of flies.

"We will take the tailor to the queen.
The queen will know how to get rid of
this tailor," said a man.

41

The people took the tailor to the queen.

The queen said, "Brave tailor, you
have scared the people in Big Town.
They want me to get rid of you.
But you can stay if you help us.
There are seven bad giants who just
moved to Big Town.
We do not want to let bad giants stay
in Big Town.
Get rid of the seven bad giants!
Then you can stay in Big Town."

"I will do that," said the tailor.
"I am not scared.
To get rid of the seven giants
I will need two things.
Let me have an egg and a bird."

The queen got an egg and a bird for
the tailor.
The tailor took the egg and the bird
from the queen.
Then he went to find the seven
giants.

43

The tailor found the seven giants.
The giants looked down and saw the
little tailor's belt.

"So, you got seven at one time," one
giant said to the tailor.

The tailor said, "Yes I did.
I can get you too!"

"You can, can you?" said the giant.

44

The biggest giant got a rock and broke
it with a big club.

"I can do better than that," said the
tailor.
"I can do that with one hand."

The tailor took the egg and broke it.
The giants did not see that it was an egg.

"You broke a rock," said a giant.

Then a giant got a little rock.

"You are strong, but can you throw a
rock like I can?" he said.
The rock went up in the sky and came
down.

"I can do better than that," said the
tailor.
He took the bird in one hand and let
it go.
The bird went up and up and up.

46

"A man that strong can get seven of
us at a time!" said the scared giants.
They ran away from the tailor.

The queen was glad to be rid of the
giants.
The little tailor was glad, too.

◆ **Think** What did people think of
the tailor when they saw the belt?

◆ **Share** What do you think was the
best thing the tailor did?

◆ **Write** Write a sentence. Tell about
something you can do.

MAKING ALL THE
CONNECTIONS

Talk About it

Look at the picture.
Think about the big things that
happened in the stories.
Think about the people and
animals in the stories.
What plans did they have?
Did the plans work?
Talk about it with the class.

Make Something Big

Think of something big.
You can work with friends to
make a picture of something big.
Here is a plan you can make with friends.

Plan with your friends
◆ What are you going to draw?
◆ How are you going to draw it?
◆ Who will draw what part?
Draw the picture of something big.
Show the picture to the class.

Pet Show

PART TWO

Something Little

Everyone was talking about
the pet show.

Using Words About Little Things

Name the little things you see in the picture.

What other little things can you tell about?

Make a Story

Use the names of little things to
finish the story.

I went to the park to find a ＿＿＿.
What I found was a ＿＿＿.
I put it in a ＿＿＿.

As You Read

In this part of the book you will
read about things that are little.
You will read about animals and
plants that are little.
You will read about people, too.

Keep a Reader's Log.
You can put in the names of little
things that you know about.
Make notes in the log about what
you read.
If you find a new word in a story,
you can put it in the log.

Little Things

It is fun to do little things for friends.
I have a friend who is sad today.
I will go and talk to my friend.
Then my friend will not be so sad.
Everyone likes to talk to a friend.

I would like to do something more for my friend.
I will read to my friend.
It is a little thing, but
it is a way to show that I care.
Everyone likes to know that they have
a friend who cares.
What little thing can you do for a friend?

The Last Puppy

by Frank Asch

I was the last of Mom's puppies.
I was the last of the puppies
to eat.
I was the last of the puppies to see.
I was the last to drink from a dish.
I was the last to go to bed at night.

I was the last puppy.
One day, a little boy came and
took the first of us puppies away.
It was not my turn.
That night I couldn't sleep very
well.
I just wanted to know:
When would it be my turn?
Would I be the last puppy?

The next day, a woman from the
town wanted to take me.
I jumped up on the woman and she
fell back into the dish.
Because she fell, the woman did
not pick me.
It was not my turn.

Next, a man came to pick a puppy.
I was so glad when the man picked
me up, I bit him.
He picked two puppies.
But he did not pick me.
It was not my turn.

One day, there were just five of
us puppies.
The next day, there were just two.
Then there was just me, the last
puppy.
Still, it was not my turn.

But then, my turn came at last.
A man picked me up and took me to
a little boy.
Then the man and the boy took me
away.

The little boy looked down at me
and I looked up at him.
He looked very glad.
He said, "Do you know what?
You are my first puppy!"

◆ **Think** Was the puppy last all of
the time?

◆ **Share** What did the puppy think
about being last?

◆ **Write** Write two sentences.
Tell when it is good to be first.
Tell when it is good to be last.

Chicken Forgets

by Miska Miles

"Chicken," the mother hen said,
"I need your help.
I need a basket of wild berries."

"I would like to get berries," the
little chicken said.

"Take this basket and fill it to the
top," the mother hen said.
"Sometimes you forget things.
THIS time, please, please don't
forget the berries."

"I will not forget," the little
chicken said.
Because he didn't want to forget,
he said over and over, "Get wild
berries.
Get wild berries."

All the way to the lake he said,
"Get wild berries."

Then the chicken saw a frog.

"What are you saying?" the frog said.

"Get wild berries," the chicken said.

"Don't say that to me," the frog said.

"What do you want me to say?" said
the chicken.

"Get a big green fly," the frog said.

The chicken went on his way.
And because he didn't want to forget,
he said, "Get a big green fly.
Get a big green fly."

All the way to the farm, he said,
"Get a big green fly."

"Don't say that to me," a goat said.

"What do you want me to say?" said
the chicken.

"Get green weeds," said the goat.

And on the chicken went, saying,
"Get green weeds.
Get green weeds."

"No, no," said a robin.
"Berries are better.
Follow me.
I will show you the place."

So the little chicken ran in the
grass, following the robin.
He came to a place where there were
many wild berries.

The robin ate and ate and ate.

And the little chicken filled his basket
with wild berries.

He went on his way home.
Back he went, by the farm and by
the lake.
He ate five berries.

Across the grass, he went.
And he ate three berries.

At home, the mother hen looked at
the basket.

"You DIDN'T forget," the mother
hen said.
"You did bring home berries and the
basket is just about filled to the top.
You are a good little chicken.
I am so glad."

And the little chicken was glad, too.

- **Think** Did the little chicken forget?

- **Share** Did the frog and the goat help the little chicken?

- **Write** Make a list. Write two things to do when you do not want to forget something.

Jamberry

One berry
Two berry
Pick me a blueberry
Hatberry
Shoeberry
In my canoeberry
Under the bridge
And over the dam
Looking for berries
Berries for jam!

Bruce Degen

70

Understanding Stories That Seem Real

Some stories that are made up
seem real.
The things that happen in the
stories are like things that could
happen in real life.

for **Jill and the New Baby** and **A Nice Little Gift**

Reading Stories That Seem Real

Stories that seem real happen
in a place that seems real.
The people in the stories are like
real people.
What happens seems real, too.

As You Read

Ask yourself: Could the things that
happen in the next two stories
happen in real life?
Look at the words in blue to help
you.

Jill and the New Baby

by Maggie Palmer

"Your mother is bringing home
your new baby sister today," said
Grandpa to Jill.

"Now I will not be the baby.
I don't like being older," said
Jill.
She felt a little sad.

Jill and Grandpa
say things that
real people
could say.

"Your mother will need you to help
care for your new baby sister,"
Grandpa said.

"What can I do to help Mother?"
said Jill.
"I am too little to help."

"You were too little, but you are
older now," said Grandpa.
"There are so many things you
can do.
You can help me now if you like."

Jill went with Grandpa to the shop.
Grandpa made things with wood in
the shop.

Think about why Grandpa wanted Jill to help.

This was the very first time that Grandpa had wanted Jill to help him make something.

"But I am too little to help you in your shop," said Jill.
"You said that I was."

"Yes, I did," said Grandpa.
"But you are older now."

Grandpa showed Jill a nice new bed made of wood.

"I made this bed for your sister,"
said Grandpa.
"But I think it needs one more
thing.
What do you think?"

Jill looked at the bed.
It was a very nice little bed made
of new wood.
She saw the one thing that
it needed.

Many people
make things
from wood in
real life.

"It needs to be painted," she said.

75

"Yes," said Grandpa.
"Will you help me paint it?"

Jill helped Grandpa to paint the bed.
They painted it blue.
When the bed was painted, Grandpa
looked at it.

"It still needs one more thing,"
he said.

Think about what
Jill will say.

"What do you think it needs,
Jill?"

Jill looked at the little bed.
She saw what it needed.
Jill got red paint.

Jill knows what to do.

"What are you going to paint,
Jill?" said Grandpa.

"You will see," said Jill.

She painted big red trucks on
the bed.

"Isn't this nice?" said Jill.

"It looks very nice.
I like the trucks best of all.
I think your new little sister is
going to like it," said Grandpa.

Jill felt glad.
She liked to think about the
little baby sleeping in the bed.

Think about
what Jill will say
or do at the end
of the story.

"Are you still sad that you are
the older sister?" said Grandpa.

"No," said Jill.
"Now that I am older, maybe I
can do more things with you.
I can help with my new sister.
It is nice to get older."

◆ **Think**   How did Grandpa help
change the way Jill felt about
the new baby?

◆ **Share**   What helped Jill be glad
about her new sister?

◆ **Write**   Write a list. Tell two
ways you could help a new baby.

A Nice Little Gift

by Noel Celsi

Maria wanted to get Mother a gift.
She went to talk to Sam about it.

"Where can I get a good gift for
my mother?" she asked Sam.

"Your mother likes plants," said Sam.
"Why don't you get your mother a
little plant at the plant store?"

Maria went to the plant store and
got a plant.
She gave the plant to Mother.

"What a nice plant!" said Mother,
when she saw it.
"And what a good gift!
Would you help me take care of
the plant, Maria?" she asked.

"Yes, I would," said Maria.

"If we take good care of this plant
it will grow," Mother said.

81

Maria and Mother took care
of the plant, but it did not
grow at all.

"Why isn't it growing?" asked
Maria at last.
"Isn't it well?"

"I don't know," said Mother.
She looked at the plant.

"There are things we can do to help the plant grow," Mother said.

First, they took the plant and moved it to a place in the sun.

"A plant needs sun to grow," said Mother.

The plant stayed in the sun for many days, but it did not grow at all.

"Now what can we do?" asked Maria.

Mother said, "A plant needs to be watered.
Maybe if we water it more, it will grow."

So Mother watered the plant.
But still the plant did not grow.

At last Mother said, "There is one
more thing to try.
The plant is in a very little pot.
We will go back to the plant store
and get a big pot.
Maybe then the plant will grow."

They went back to the plant store.
They found a big pot in the store and
took it home.
They put the plant in the big pot,
watered it, and put it in the sun.

Then the plant did grow!
How the plant did grow!

"This plant looks like it will grow into
a tree!" said Maria.

She and Mother looked at the plant.

"That plant is too big for the house,"
said Mother.
"We cannot have a plant that big
in this little house.
What can we do?"

"It was a nice little plant when
you gave it to me," said Mother.
"Now look at it!"

"I know what we can do," said Maria.
"We can cut pieces from the plant.
The pieces will make new little plants.
The little plants will make nice
gifts for everyone we know."

And that is what they did.
They cut little pieces from
the big plant.
Next, they gave the little pieces
away as gifts.
Everyone who got a piece of the plant
was glad to get a nice little gift.

◆ **Think**   What made Maria's gift
grow?

◆ **Share**   What could Maria do if the
plant got big again?

◆ **Write**   Write a sentence. Tell about
a good gift that you can make.

MAKING ALL THE
CONNECTIONS

Talk About Little Things

Look at the picture.
Think about the little things in the
stories.
What little things can grow?
How do the people and animals
grow and do new things?

The
Last
Puppy

Chicken
Forgets

Jill
and the
New
Baby

A
Nice
Little
Gift

Read Something New

Look at Andy in the pictures.
Read what Andy writes.

When I was a baby, I was very little.
I could ride on my mother's back.
I liked to look at all the birds.

Now that I am older, I am bigger.
I can run and jump.
I can play ball with my friends.

What did Andy do when he was
little?
What can he do now?

MAKING ALL THE CONNECTIONS

Think About the Stories

Here are some people from the stories about little things.
Use the words in the box to tell what the people like to do.

birds   ball
gift   painted a bed

1. When Andy was little, he liked to look at the ____.
2. Now Andy can hit a ____.
3. Jill was glad when she ____.
4. Maria gave a ____.

The first two sentences are about Andy.
Think about what you did when you were little and what you do now.
Now it is time to write about you and what you can do.

Write a Story About You

A story can tell about many things.
You can write a story that tells
about you.

Plan   Think of something you
liked to do when you were little.
Think of something you like to do now.
Draw pictures to show the things
you liked to do then and now.

Write   Now write your story:
1. When I was little, I liked to _____.
2. Now, I like to _____.

Check   Can you read your story?
Did you write **I** with a capital letter?
Did you start each sentence with a
capital letter?

Save your story and your pictures.
You can start a book.
Call it *A Book About Me*.
You can write more in your book.

Blueberries for Sal

PART THREE

On the
Land

Blueberries for me!

Using Words About the Land

Name the things in the picture that you could find on the land.

What other things could you find on the land?

What can people and animals do on the land?

Make a Story

Use the names of things on the
land to finish the story.

Today, I walked on a ____.
I came to a ____.
I jumped down from a ____.

As You Read

In this part of the book you will
read about things on the land.
You will read about people and
animals who make things and
do things.

Keep a Reader's Log.
You can put in the names of land
things you know about.
Make notes in the log about what
you read.
If you find a new word in a story,
you can put it in the log.

Stories About the Land

There are so many things on the land.

There are things near to home.

There are things far from home.

There are people and animals.

There are plants growing.

I like to read stories about the land.

People and animals need to get from place to place on the land.
People go far away from home.
They go to see new things.
But you can see new things near to home, too.
When I stop and look, there are new things to see near my home.
If you stay near to home and if you go far away, you can see something new on the land.

This Could Be a Garden

by Eve Feldman

Cast:

Narrator	**Sam**
Jill	**Pat**

Narrator: One warm day, Jill, Sam, and Pat were playing.

Jill: Look at this lot.

Sam: I wish it didn't look so bad.

Pat: How did it get like this?

Jill: We could fix this lot up.
     We could make it into a garden.
     People and animals could come
     to the garden.

Pat: Animals come to this lot.

Sam: Look at all the ants.

Jill: Stop it, you two!
     We can make this nice.

Narrator: Pat and Sam looked at Jill as she went into the lot and started to pick up things.

Jill: Are you going to just look? We will have fun if you help.

Narrator: Sam and Pat ran to help.

Jill: Maybe we can make a birdhouse from things we find around the lot.

Sam: Birds need to drink, too.
I will make something that
birds can drink from.

Narrator: Sam looked around the
lot.

Sam: This is what I need!
If I can make this stay up,
the birds will have a place
to drink.
There, I did it!

Pat: We still need a birdhouse.
I don't know how to make one.

Narrator: Pat looked around at all the
things that were left in the
lot.

Pat: Save that wood for me.
I will find a book that will
tell me how to make a
birdhouse!

Narrator: Jill, Sam, and Pat worked
for days and days.
First, they had to throw away
many things.
A truck took away all the
things that they did not need.

Jill: That looks better.
Now we can start the fun work.

Narrator: They planted grass in the lot
and fixed it up.

Pat: I found a book about how to
make a birdhouse.
We can make it from the
wood that was left in the lot.

Narrator: Everyone helped.
Soon there was a birdhouse in a
tree and grass in the garden.
On warm days, people could
come to sit in the garden
and look at the birds.

Jill: We made a garden!
Now all we need is a lake.
Who wants to help me make
a lake?

Sam and Pat: Not me!

◆ **Think** How did Jill, Pat, and Sam
make the lot into a garden?

◆ **Share** Do you think the garden
needs a lake?

◆ **Write** Make a list.
Write three things people can do
in a garden.

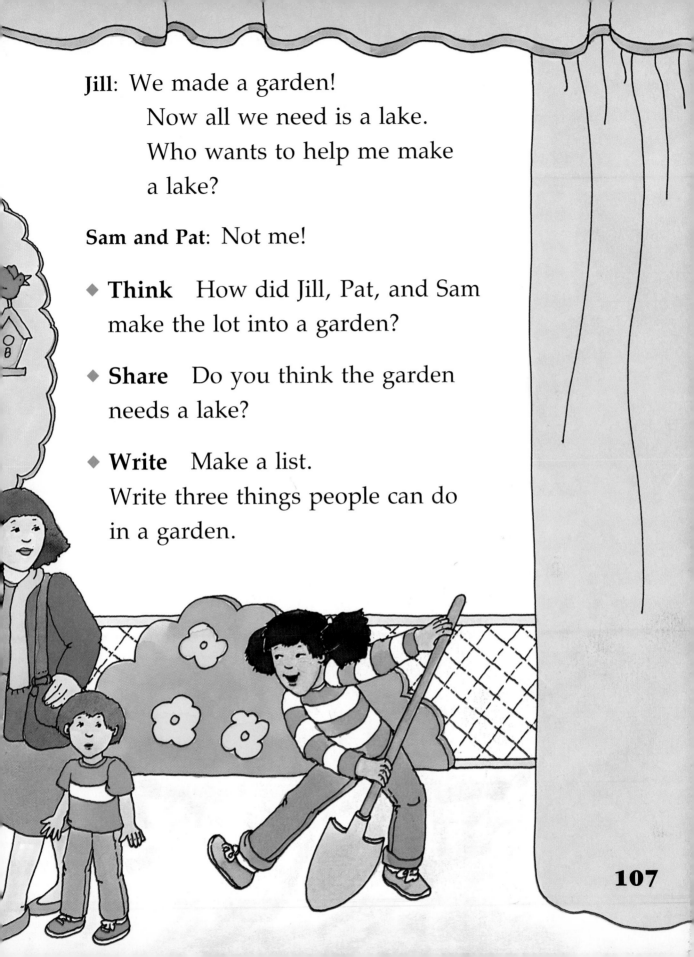

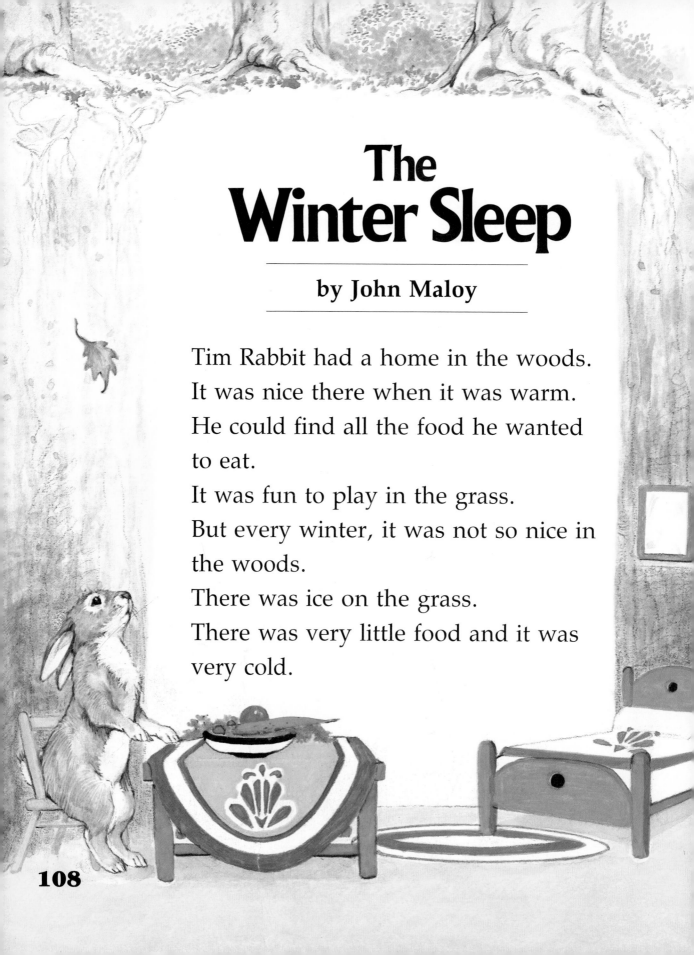

The
Winter Sleep

by John Maloy

Tim Rabbit had a home in the woods.
It was nice there when it was warm.
He could find all the food he wanted
to eat.
It was fun to play in the grass.
But every winter, it was not so nice in
the woods.
There was ice on the grass.
There was very little food and it was
very cold.

One day, Tim Rabbit saw Max Bear.
Tim Rabbit said, "My friends and I
don't like the winter.
There is all that ice, and we cannot
find food."

Max Bear said, "I like winter.
When it gets cold, I eat more food.
Then I go into my warm home and I
sleep all winter."

This made Tim Rabbit think.

Tim Rabbit went to see Fran Rabbit.
Tim Rabbit said, "Bears have a good
time every winter.
They sleep."

"I wish we could sleep every winter,
too," said Fran Rabbit.

Tim and Fran Rabbit went to talk to
Max Bear.

Max Bear said, "I would be glad to let
you sleep at my house all winter.
I will tell you what we must do to
have a good sleep.
First, we must get very tired."

"How will we get tired?" asked Fran
Rabbit.

Max Bear said, "One way to get tired
is to run fast."

"We do not run," said Tim Rabbit. "We hop."

So, Tim and Fran hopped around and around the woods, but they did not get tired.

Max Bear said, "Maybe it would help if you found something dull to do."

Fran said, "We can go see Nat Turtle!"

Max Bear said, "Nat Turtle could make
a rock yawn."

So Fran and Tim went to see Nat Turtle.
The plan worked.
Nat Turtle could not stop telling
dull stories.

Soon Tim and Fran Rabbit got tired.
They yawned and said goodnight, but
Nat Turtle went on telling dull stories
to the trees.

Back at home, Max Bear had food and
warm drinks for Tim and Fran.
He ran around singing a song.
He was so glad to have friends come
to stay with him.

In the woods, it got very cold.
But Max's home was nice and warm,
just as Max had said it would be.
Tim and Fran Rabbit were telling
bedtime stories.

For a time, Max Bear was scared that Tim and Fran Rabbit would not get to sleep.

Max said, "I would be glad to show you my home movies."

But Tim and Fran did not think that movies would be fun.

Max sang a bedtime song.
Tim and Fran yawned and yawned.
They all fell into a good sleep.

Tim and Fran got up.
Max Bear was still sleeping.
It was still winter.

"What can we do?" asked Fran.

"Maybe we could look at the home
movies now," Tim said to Fran.

116

Tim and Fran stayed in Max's house
all winter.
At night they went to sleep.
Every day, they looked at movies.
They had a good winter.

◆ **Think** Why did Tim and Fran want
to stay with Max all winter?

◆ **Share** What do you think the
rabbits will do when it gets warm?

◆ **Write** Write a sentence. Tell what
you can do to help you go to sleep.

Grandpa Bear's Lullaby

The night is long
But fur is deep.
You will be warm
In winter sleep.

The food is gone
But dreams are sweet
And they will be
Your winter meat.

The cave is dark
But dreams are bright
And they will serve
As winter light.

Sleep, my little cubs, sleep.

Jane Yolen

Understanding the Big Idea

Stories tell about people, animals, and places.
Stories tell about things that happen.
Most stories have a big idea.
The big idea is what a story is all about.

for **Bikes** and **Travel in the City**

Thinking About the Big Idea

Read this story.
What is it all about?

José likes to look at birds.
He likes to look at bluebirds.
He likes to look at eagles.
He likes to look at ducks best.

As You Read

Ask yourself: What are the big ideas in the next two stories?
There is a big idea on every page.
Use the words in blue to help you.

119

Bikes

by Lewis L. Symonds

This tells about the first bikes.

The first bikes were not like the bikes of today.
They were very hard to ride.
They did not have pedals.

To make the bikes go fast, people had to ride down a hill.
At times, people would fall.
It was hard to stop!
The bikes were not very safe.

120

Then, in 1839, a man had a good idea.
This idea was to make a bike with
pedals.
When people moved the pedals, the
wheels of the bike moved.

Pedals made things better, but it was
still hard to ride a bike.
People could now ride bikes up a hill.
The new bikes could go fast.
At times, the bikes went *too* fast.
People would fall.

Think about
what happened
to the bikes
when they
got pedals.

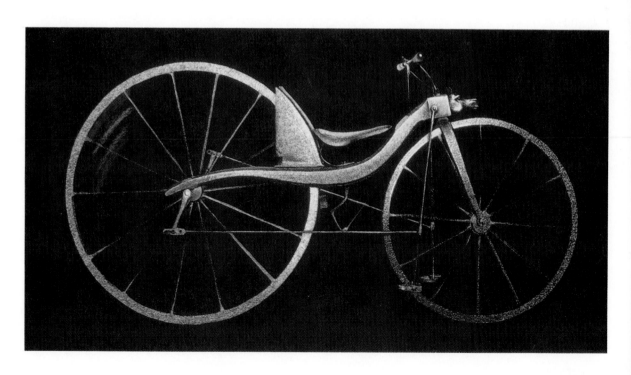

Then, in 1871, a man had a new idea about how to make a bike.
The front wheel of the bike was very big.
The back wheel was very little.
To ride this bike, people had to get up on the big front wheel.
This was hard to do.
It was fun to sit up on the big front wheel and ride.

By 1880, bikes started to look more
like they look today.
The front wheel was not so big.
The back wheel was not so little.
Bikes were safe and not so hard to ride.

Now many people could ride bikes.
People went to see bike races.
There were bikes that two people
could ride.
Bikes were everywhere.

Think about the
two big ideas
on this page.

123

Today, people still ride bikes.
Some people ride bikes to work.
Some people ride bikes for fun.
Bikes take people many places.

◆ **Think** How are today's bikes not like the older bikes?

◆ **Share** What bike do you think was the most fun to ride?

◆ **Write** Draw a picture of a new idea for a bike. Write a sentence that tells about the picture.

from

Bike Ride

Look!
Our bikes
spin
black-and-white
shadow
pinwheels.

Lilian Moore

Travel in the City

by Daniel Lewis

A city can be very big.
It is made up of many people and
places.
There are many things to do.

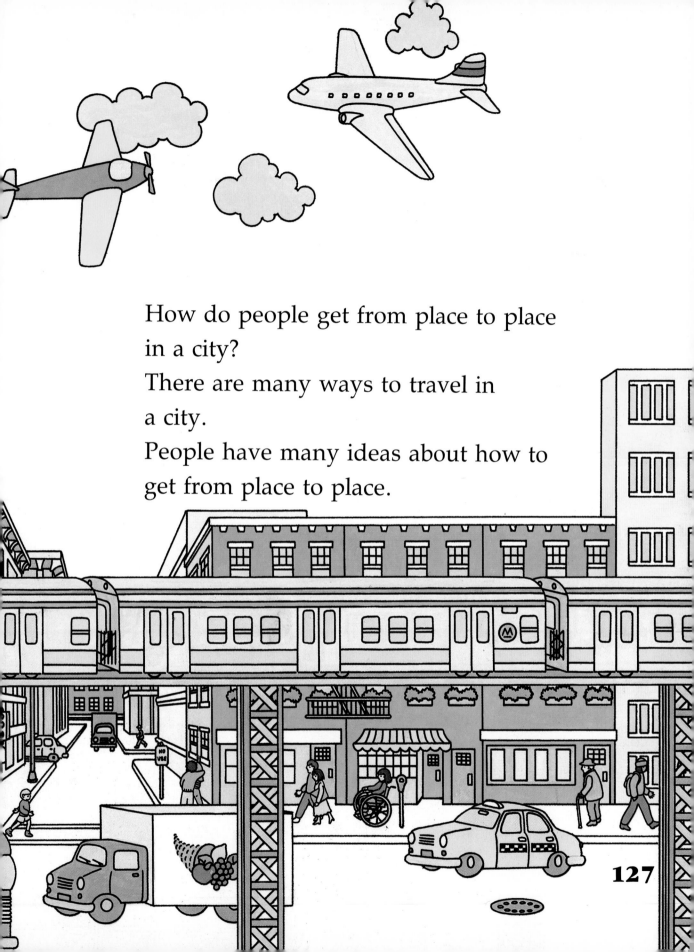

How do people get from place to place
in a city?
There are many ways to travel in
a city.
People have many ideas about how to
get from place to place.

127

A nice way to travel in a city is to
walk.

There are so many things to see.

Walking can be the best way to travel
if you are not in a hurry.

People walk in a city and look at
stores.

They look to see what is playing at the
movies.

People walk to the park and to the
zoo.

They can walk to see friends.

If you ride on a bus you can go many places in a city.
The bus can take you places that are too far to walk to.
Each day, a bus drives up and down a city's streets.
It makes many stops.

Many people ride a bus to work.
They ride the bus to go home at night.
Sometimes, so many people get on a bus that some people cannot sit.

Cars ride the city streets, too.
When people drive cars, they have to
find a place to put the car.
Sometimes it is hard to find a place.
Still, many people drive cars in a city.
Each day, people drive cars to work,
to see friends, to parks and to
the zoo.

Sometimes, there are so many cars
and buses on the streets that they
cannot move very fast.
That is why one of the best ways to
travel in a city can be by train.
Trains do not travel on the city's
streets.
They run on tracks.
Many people can ride on a train at
one time.

Some people fly around a city.
It is a very fast way to get from place
to place.
People can fly to where help is needed.

Some people who fly around a city
look down at the streets.
They look for places where there are
too many cars and buses.

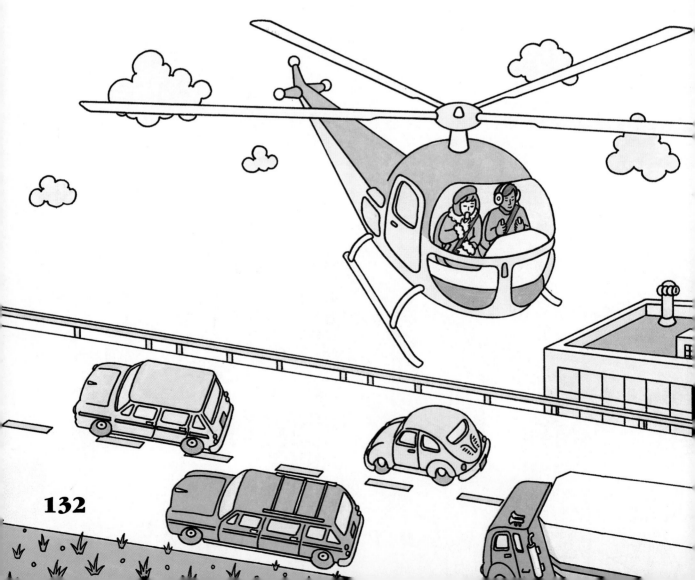

People need to get from place to place
in a city.
They can pick where they want to go.
They can pick how they will get there.

◆ **Think** How do people get around
in a city?

◆ **Share** What way of traveling in a
city do you like the best?

◆ **Write** Write a sentence. Tell what
you like best about a ride on a bus.

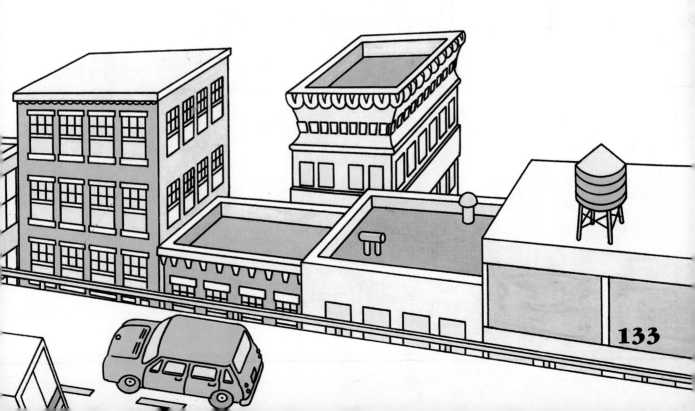

MAKING ALL THE
CONNECTIONS

Talk About It

Look at the picture.
Think about the things on the land
that are in the stories.
What happens on the land?
What do the people in the stories
make and do?
What do you like the best?

Make a Garden

One thing people can do on land
is make a garden.
You can make a garden, too.
This is what you will need:

1. Draw some plants to put in your
   garden.
2. Cut out the plants.
3. Tape the plants to a piece of
   paper.
4. Fold the plants out so that
   they will stand up.

Now you have made a nice garden!

The Owl and the Pussy-cat

PART FOUR

On the Sea

They sailed away for a year and a day.

Using Words About the Sea

Name the things in the picture that
you could see around the sea.
What other things could you
see on and in the sea?
What can people and animals do on
the sea?

Make a Story

Use words about the sea to finish the story.

Jill went sailing on a ____.
She saw a big ____.
She could hear the ____.

As You Read

In this part of the book you will read about things in the water. You will read about animals in the water and people on the water. You will read about the water, too!

Keep a Reader's Log. You can put in the names of sea things you know about. Make notes in the log about what you read. If you find a new word in a story, you can put it in the log.

What Is in the Water

Water is all around the land.

Many fish, plants, and animals are in the water.

In the water, fish swim in schools.

You can see schools of fish in the water.

You can swim in the water.

You can sail on the water, too.

People have found many things in the
water.
Some of the things stayed in the water
for years and years.
Come sail and swim with me!
We can have fun!
There are many things to see
and do.

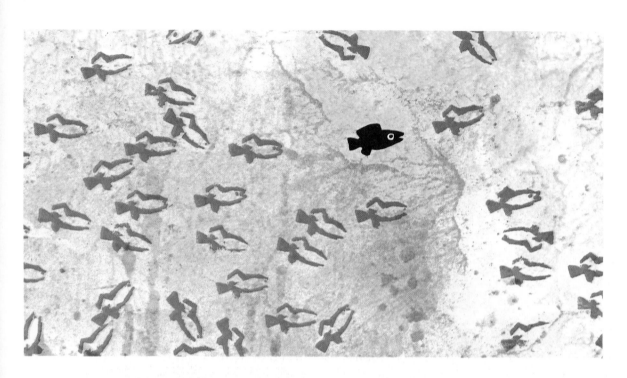

Swimmy

by Leo Lionni

A happy school of little fish lived in
the sea somewhere.
They were all red.
Only one of them was black.
He swam faster than his brothers and
sisters.
His name was Swimmy.

One bad day a tuna fish came.
He swallowed all the little red fish.
Only Swimmy escaped.

He swam away.
He was scared and very sad.
But the sea was full of wonderful
creatures, and as he swam Swimmy
was happy.

He saw a lobster, who walked about
like a water-moving machine . . .
a forest of seaweed growing from
sugar-candy rocks . . .
and an eel whose tail was almost
too far away to remember.

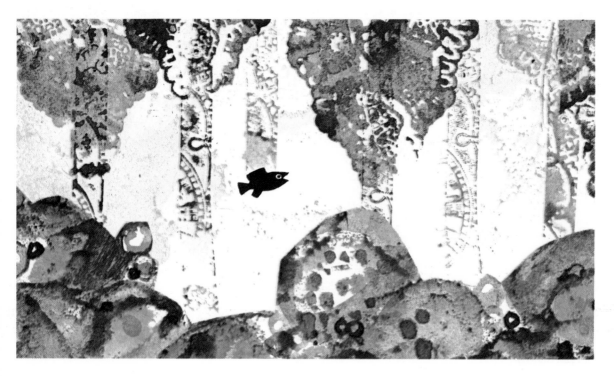

Then, in the dark shade of rocks, he
saw a school of little fish, just like his
own.

"Let us go and swim and play and
SEE things!" he said.

"We can't," said the little red fish.
"The big fish will eat us all."

"But you can't just lie there," said
Swimmy.
"We must THINK of something."
Then he said, "I have it!
We are going to swim all together like
the biggest fish in the sea!"

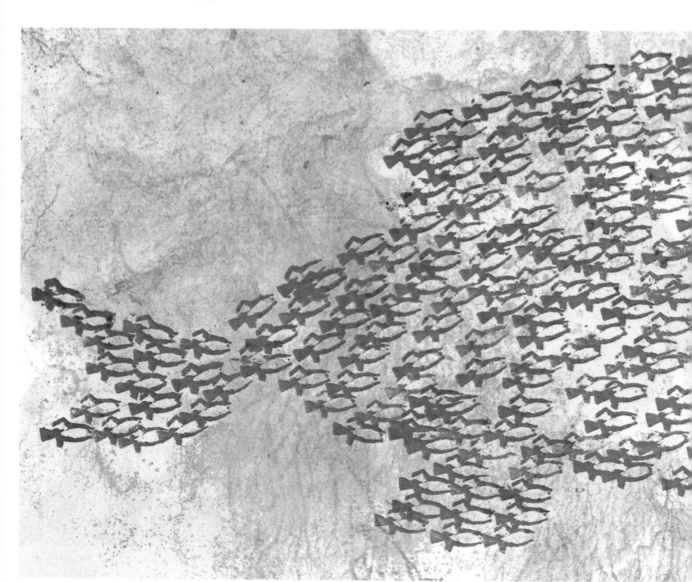

He taught them to swim close
together, each in his own place. When
they had learned to swim like one
giant fish, he said, "I will be the eye."

And so they swam and chased the big
fish away.

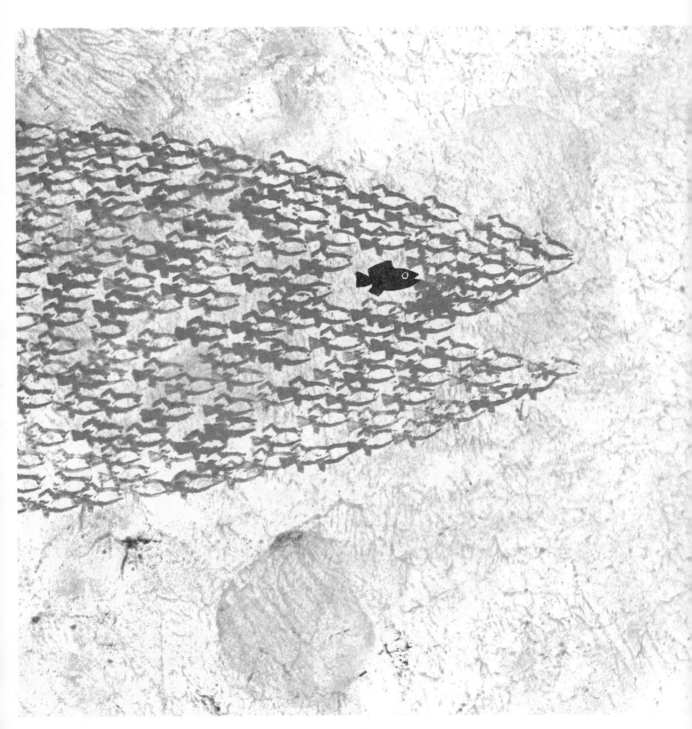

◆ **Think** Why do you think that Swimmy was the eye?

◆ **Share** What part of Swimmy's story did you like the best? Read it to the class.

◆ **Write** Draw a picture. In your picture, show a wonderful place Swimmy and his friends could go.

The Sun and the Sea

**an African tale retold
by Sarudzai Hove**

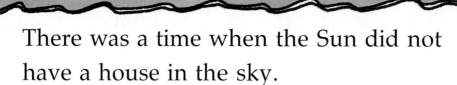

There was a time when the Sun did not
have a house in the sky.
The Sun had a house by the Sea.
The Sun and the Sea were good friends.

The Sun went to the Sea's house again
and again.
But the Sea never once went to the
Sun's house.

After a time, the Sun said,
"I come to see you all the time but
you never once have come to see me.
Why not?
I have a nice house."
The Sun seemed sad.

The Sea said, "You have no idea how
many children I have.
You have a little house.
I never come because your house is
too little for me and all my children."

But still the Sun seemed sad.
The Sun asked the Sea to come to the
house many times.

At last, the Sea went to see the Sun.
"I have come to see you.
May I come in?" the Sea asked.

"Yes, my friend," the Sun said.

"May I come in with all my children?"
the Sea asked.

"Yes, come in with all your children,"
the Sun said.

And so the Sea started to come in,
with all the green waters.
In came the red, blue, and green fish.
In came the big and little animals.

After a little time the water came up to
the Sun's feet.
Soon it came up to the Sun's face.

The Sea asked, "May I still come in?"

155

The Sun did not know what to say.
After all, the Sun was the one who
had wanted the Sea to come.
The Sun's hands and feet were now in
the water.
All of the Sun's face would soon be in
the water.
Not knowing what to do, the Sun got
on top of the little house.
After that, the Sun said, "Yes, yes, do
come in."

Once the waters of the Sea came up to the top of the house, the Sun had to jump up in the blue sky.
The Sun never came back down again.

◆ **Think** What happened when the Sea went to the Sun's house?

◆ **Share** Do you think it was a good thing that the Sea went to the Sun's house?

◆ **Write** Write a sentence.
Tell what you think the Sun's house looked like after the Sea and all the children came in.

Until I Saw the Sea

Until I saw the sea
I did not know
that wind
could wrinkle the water so.

I never knew
that sun
could splinter the whole sea of blue.

Nor
did I know before,
a sea breathes in and out
upon a shore.

Lilian Moore

159

Meet Lilian Moore

Would you like to meet a poet? Lilian Moore likes to write stories, but most of all she likes to write poems. The poems "Bike Ride" and "Until I Saw the Sea" are by Lilian Moore.

She wants people to have fun when they read the poems she writes. A book of poems you can read is "I Feel The Same Way."

Here is a poem by Lilian Moore that tells why she is glad to be a poet:

Poets look at what they see
   As if it were new
Then in their poems they tell us
   "You look too!"

Understanding Stories That Are True

True stories tell about things that are real.

True stories tell about real people, real places, and real animals.

for **A Look at Whales** and **Treasure Under the Sea**

Reading Stories That Are True

Things are not made up in true stories.

When you read a true story, there are times when you must read more slowly.

There are many ideas and things to think about.

As You Read

Ask yourself: How can I tell that the next two stories are about real people, places, or animals?

Use the words in blue to help you.

A Look at Whales

by Elizabeth West

This is a true story. It tells about real animals.

Do you know about whales?
Whales, like fish, are in the sea.
They look like very big fish, but they are not fish at all.
Whales cannot stay under the water all the time, as fish do.
They have to come up for air.

This is a whale.
This whale is very big, but it just eats little things.
It gets food from water.
The whale takes a big drink of water.
The little plants and animals that the whale eats are in the water.

This tells about the whale.

Do not read this too fast.
There are many things to think about.

Whales can swim well.

They come up for air, and then they swim down in the water.

They can stay under water for a time but then they have to come back up for air.

Far down in the sea, away from the sun, the water looks black.

How do whales get around in the dark water?

Do whales have eyes that can see in the dark or do they use the sounds in the water?

Under water, whales do not have eyes that see in the dark.
Whales use sound.
A whale makes a sound, again and again.
If something is not far away, the whale's sound will reach it.
When the sound comes back to the whale it tells the whale where that thing is.
Sound helps keep whales safe.

Think about how whales use sound.

People think that whales use sound to tell where a shore is.
They need to know where a shore is.
It is not safe for whales to go on land.
Whales use sound to keep away from the land.

At times, some whales jump up into the air.
Is this just for fun or is it a game?
It looks like a wonderful game.

Some whales make sounds and play
with people in the water.
Many people think that whales do this
to show they are happy.
People want to know about whales.
That is why people look at whales.

◆ **Think**　How are whales like fish?
How are whales not like fish?

◆ **Share**　Why do you think some
whales like to jump out of the water?

◆ **Write**　Write a question. What do
you want to know about whales?

Treasure Under the Sea

by Jay Bastible

In 1545, there was a king who liked
ships.
He had a big ship made.
It took a very long time to make this
ship.
No ship was as big as this one.

At last, the ship could go out on the water.
Many ships were with it.
The king looked at his big ship as it went out to sea.
He was very happy.

All at once, a big wind came up.
Water went into the big ship.
The ship went down.

The king had some people make maps
to show where his ship was.
The king wanted to find the ship.
The king wanted the things that were
in the ship.

The maps showed where the ship was,
but no one could reach it.
The ship was too far down in the
water.
People could not see in the water
because it was not clean.

For a very long time, the ship stayed
in the water.
Then in 1965, a man found the old
maps.
People could now do many more
things under water.
There were ways to get air under
water and to see in the water.

People went again and again to look
for the ship, but they could not find it.

A prince came to look for the ship.
The prince went down in the water,
but could not find the ship.

After a long time, in 1971, someone
found the ship.
The prince was very happy.

There was a treasure of wonderful old
things in the ship.

People took good care of the treasure
in the ship.
They found out what each thing was.
Then they cleaned each piece.
People would come and look at the
treasure.

But the people wanted to bring the
ship out of the water, too.
This was a big job.
The ship was big and very old.

They looked for a long time.
At last, they found something that
could help bring the ship to the top of
the water.
It was very big.
The people who had it said they could
bring up the old ship.

They had to wait for the water to be
very still.
The people waited for many days.

The big day came at last, in 1982.
Many people came in little boats to see
the big ship.

The prince was there in a little boat, too.

The ship came up in one piece.
The king's ship and all of the treasure had come to shore at last.

◆ **Think** Why did it take so long to get the things in the ship?

◆ **Share** Why do you think the king wanted so big a ship?

◆ **Write** Make a list. List three treasures you would like to find in an old ship.

MAKING ALL THE
CONNECTIONS

Talk About the Sea

Look at the picture.
Think about all the things in and on
the sea that were in the stories.
What did you find out about the sea?
What story did you like best?

Read Something New

Look at the pictures.
Read the story.

There was a puppy named Dot.
All Dot's friends could swim, but
she couldn't.
Dot's friends gave Dot a boat.
When they went swimming,
Dot could follow in the boat.

Dot had a problem.
What was it?
How did it get fixed?

MAKING ALL THE CONNECTIONS

Think About the Stories

Most stories tell about problems and how they get fixed.
Finish the sentences to tell how the problems are fixed.

1. Dot's friends gave Dot a ____.
2. Swimmy and the red fish swam close ____.
3. The sun jumped into the ____.
4. To find things in dark water, whales use ____.
5. It took a long time to get the treasure from under the sea because ____.

That first sentence is about how Dot's problem was fixed.
Think about a problem.
What is it?
How could it get fixed?
Now it is time for you to write a story about fixing a problem.

Write a Story

Stories are fun to write.
You can write a story that shows
how to fix a problem.

Plan Think of who will be in your story.
Think of what the problem will be.
Think of how the problem will be fixed.
Draw pictures to show your ideas.

Write Now write your story:
1. Tell who the story is about.
2. Tell what the problem is.
3. Tell how the problem gets fixed.

Check Can you read your story?
Did you start all special names with
a capital letter?
Do you like your story?

Share Tell your story to your
friends.
You can show your pictures, too.

Read the sentences.
Look at the pictures.
They will help you understand
the words in dark print.

<u>Aa</u>

ant   The **ant** is a very little
             animal.

ate   I **ate** the food Mom made.

Bb

berries   We went to the woods to
pick wild **berries**.

boat   A **boat** can travel on water,
but not on land.

Cc

children   **Children** like to play.

city   A **city** has more people than
a town.

181

Dd

dark   It gets too **dark** to see at night.

drive   Many people **drive** cars in the city.

Ee

egg   You can eat an **egg.**

eyes   My **eyes** are blue.

Ff

first   If you come in **first** you
            win the race.

food   You can get this **food** in the
            store.

Gg

giant   A **giant** must have a very
            big house.

grass   There is not a lot of green
            grass in the city.

Hh

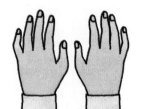

hands   I play the drum with my **hands**.

hill   It is not very easy to run up a **hill**.

Ii

ice   Water turns to **ice** when it is very, very cold.

Jj

job   My mother works at a **job** in the city.

184

Kk

king   When the prince grows up, he will be the **king**.

Ll

land   The grass made the **land** look very green.

long   The giraffe has a very **long** neck.

Mm

move   We are going to **move** to a new house.

Nn

nice   It is **nice** to be with a friend.

Oo

older   Your Mom is **older** than you.

one   I have **one** red shoe and one blue shoe.

Pp

parade   Many people can be in a
              parade.

pedals   I have green **pedals** on my
               bike.

Qq

queen   The **queen** is the mother
              of the prince.

187

Rr

ride   You can **ride** a horse.

ring   She has a **ring** on one hand.

Ss

sea   The **sea** has waves.

stories   **Stories** can tell about far
               away places.

Tt

together   We will have fun if we sing **together**.

treasure   It would be nice to find some **treasure**.

Uu

under   We sat **under** the tree.

Vv

van   We can all fit in the **van**.

189

Ww

whale   A **whale** is a very big sea animal.

Yy

yawn   I **yawn** when I am tired.

Zz

zoo   There are many animals in the **zoo.**

190

Word List

191

Word List